CONTENTS

Published 2022. Little Brother Books Ltd, Ground Floor, 23 Southernhay East, Exeter, Devon EX1 1QL

books@littlebrotherbooks.co.uk | www.littlebrotherbooks.co.uk

Printed in the United Kingdom

The Little Brother Books trademark, email and website addresses, are the sole and exclusive properties of Little Brother Books Limited.

ONLINE ACTIVITIES

On some of the pages you will see QR codes. These QR codes take you to online Purple Mash activities which support learning from the relevant page.

To use the QR codes, scan the QR code with the camera on your web enabled tablet, click on the link and the activity will appear on screen.

Alternatively, QR readers are available on the app store for your device.

SCAN CODE

purple mash

PARTS OF A SENTENCE

The Loud House is a crazy collection of people and actions.

Nouns are words that refer to a person, place, thing or event.
Verbs are action or doing words.

1

Look at the words below. Can you identify the **nouns** and **verbs**?
Circle all the nouns and underline all the verbs.

reading	loud	ball	dangerous	pointing	pranking
chaos	running	sporty	tongue	telephone	liquid
under	spider	sunglasses	baby rattle	guitar	calmly
noisy	test tube	Lincoln	door	yelling	angrily
hat	chatting	over	catching	playing	green

2

Adjectives are used to describe the noun in more detail.
Lori is texting on her glittery phone.
Underline the **adjective** in these sentences:

a. Lincoln's room is a large closet.

b. Leni likes a pretty outfit.

c. Luna has written a rock song.

d. Luan placed a silly whoopee cushion on the couch.

e. Lily has a smelly diaper.

> Phone is the **noun** so glittery is the **adjective** because it describes the phone.

3

Adverbs describe the word in the sentence that is the verb, an adjective or another adverb. They give information about the action such as how, when or where the action was done.

Lincoln and Lynn ran quickly.

'Quickly' is the adverb; it explains how they ran.

Use an adverb to complete these sentences.

a. Luan plays the guitar _____.

b. Lynn loves to play sports _____.

c. Leni always dresses _____.

d. Lisa _____ works on her experiment.

HANDWRITING PRACTICE

Sometimes, Luna writes down song lyrics so fast that she can't read her handwriting afterwards!

Ascenders include all capital letters and the lower-case letters which reach the top line such as l, t and k. **Descenders** sit on the line, but part fall below the line you are writing on, such as p, q and g. When handwriting, you must ensure that you space your words out so that the ascenders of the line below do not obstruct the descenders from the line above.

1 Practise writing out the **ascenders** and **descenders**. Be sure they are spaced appropriately.

Ascenders

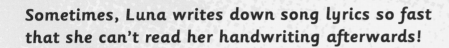

bb   dd   hh   kk   ll   tt

Descenders

gg   pp   qq   yy   jj   yy

2 Luna is trying to work out what lyrics she has written in her notebook. Can you help her by writing out the words in your best handwriting?

 guitar   song    jam

guitar   song   jam

3

HOMOPHONES AND NEAR HOMOPHONES

Being twins, Lana and Lola may sound similar, but they are actually VERY different.

Homophones are words that sound the same but have different spellings and meanings. A **near homophone** is a word which is pronounced almost the same as another word but has a different spelling and meaning.

1 Help the twins to make a match. Draw a line to link the **homophones**. The first one has been done for you.

pear	meat	ball	break	great	herd	knight	blue

bawl	night	pair	brake	heard	blew	meet	grate

2 Circle the **homophone** which makes these sentences correct.

a. Lincoln wants to meet / meat Clyde in the park.

b. Lori missed / mist Bobby's call and felt sad.

c. Lisa's experiment blue / blew up.

d. This will be a great / grate plan if Lincoln and Clyde can make it work.

e. Lori herd / heard Luan talking to Lincoln about her next prank.

3 Write out the pairs of **near homophones** next to each other in the table. The first one has been done for you.

~~quiet~~
were
further
accept
bury

Near homophones	
quiet	quite

berry
father
where
except
~~quite~~

READING COMPREHENSION

Leni is dreaming of a new dress. Read the text below then answer the questions about it. Remember to pay attention to the details of what you read and develop a picture of it in your head – this will help you to understand the text better.

Leni's new dress

Leni was designing a new dress. She walked outside, dreaming of her new outfit and instantly fell over the recycling that was left on the porch. She looked at the cardboard scattered all around her and had an idea: Her new dress could be made of cardboard boxes!

Leni designed and created her new dress and proudly modelled it for Lincoln, who was playing with a ball outside. Lincoln thought the dress still looked too boxy. Leni looked around for something else to use and spied the flowery tablecloth on the kitchen table.

Leni was able to use her style skills to fashion a dress from the tablecloth.

Later that afternoon, Lynn Sr. came into the kitchen and was puzzled about where the tablecloth had gone? He asked the family and Leni kept very quiet but had the thought that she should have created an outfit out of something else!

Leni planned to carefully replace the tablecloth later, as she pondered about what she could use for her dress instead. She then saw Dad taking a box of old things to the garage. She noticed that there was something sparkly in the box.

Once the area was empty of people, she crept to the garage and discovered an antique chandelier. She created the most sparkly dress out of the old chandelier which amazed and dazzled everyone.

1 — Answer the true or false questions by putting a tick in the correct box.

	TRUE	FALSE
a. Leni wanted to make a new hat.		
b. Lincoln was walking the dog.		
c. One of the dresses was made of cardboard.		
d. One of Leni's dresses was made of a tablecloth.		
e. Dad had the object which Leni make her final dress out of.		
f. Everyone was amazed by the final outfit.		

2 — Write a sentence to answer these questions.

a. What three types of materials did Leni use for her dresses?

_____

b. Which characters helped Leni to develop her ideas?

_____

c. Explain why Leni decided not to use the tablecloth.

_____

DIRECT SPEECH

There's always plenty of direct speech happening in the Loud house!

The ball flew over the fence into Mr. Grouse's garden.

"It's your turn to sneak into his garden and get it," said Lincoln.

"No way!" said Clyde, "you threw the ball so you should get it!"

This is an example of direct speech. Direct speech is a way to write exactly what the characters in the story say. Here are some tips for writing direct speech:

Speech marks: The words that are spoken are punctuated with inverted commas.

New speaker, new line: Each time the speaker changes, you should start a new line to make it clear that a different person is speaking.

Reporting clause: This is the writing that says who has spoken, there should be punctuation (a comma, question mark, exclamation mark etc.) between the direct speech and the reporting clause.

1

Punctuate these direct speech sentences by putting in their missing inverted commas around the spoken words. The first one has been done for you.

a. "Where's Cliff the cat?" asked Mum.

b. I love you, Lori! swooned Bobby.

c. I'm a rock star, shouted Luna.

d. Who broke the car? yelled Lynn Sr.

e. I love it when a prank comes together! laughed Luan.

2

You can make your direct speech more interesting for the reader by not always using the word 'said' in the reporting clause. How many other words could you use?

whispered

cried

shouted

INDEFINITE ARTICLES

Lori is tidying up the kitchen and searching for whatever it is that has stunk out the room. She thinks it's another of Lily's horrible diapers!

Articles refer to items (nouns) when talking or writing. There are **definite articles**, such as **the** table (meaning a specific table) and **indefinite articles** of **a** or **an**, such as **a** pen (meaning any pen). If a word starts with a **vowel sound**, use **an** and if the word starts with a **consonant** sound, use **a**.

1

Lori is making a list of the items that she can see in the kitchen. Choose 6 items, add them to the list and use the correct **indefinite article** for each item.

_____   _____

_____   _____

_____   _____

2

Some words start with a letter which makes a sound different to its letter sound. For example: 'It was **an honest** mistake.' The **h** makes a vowel sound **'o'** so you use **'an'** despite h being a consonant. Put **'a'** or **'an'** before these words. **Top tip:** listen carefully to the starting sound of the word before you decide.

a. _____ x-ray   b. _____ honour   c. _____ uniform   d. _____ hour

SPELLING PATTERN -CIAN

Lisa is not sure what she wants to be when she grows up - a scientist, robotic engineer or maybe just an evil genius who takes over the world...

All words have spelling patterns. Words with the **-cian** spelling pattern often indicate a skilled occupation.

1 Add the **-cian** ending to these occupations.
Draw a line to match the occupation with the description.

a. An eye specialist

b. A doctor

c. Plays an instrument

d. Performs tricks

e. Works with electricity

f. Works with makeup

physi _____

beauti _____

magi _____

electri _____

opti _____

musi _____

2 Unscramble these occupations using the hints:

a. Elected to run the country   ploitician _____

b. Very good with numbers   iahetmmtacian _____

c. Might fix the computers at school   iecthncian _____

d. Advises on healthy eating   eidtician _____

SIMILES

Lynn is as fast as a speeding train as she wins the race, Lola is as beautiful as a rainbow when she enters a pageant and Lisa is as smart as a brain surgeon when she is inventing things.

When writing descriptively, you can use **similes** to help the reader develop a picture of what is happening. Similes compare something with something else and use the word **as** or **like**.

1 Match the simile to the correct Loud House character. The first one has been done for you.

As calm as the sea on a summer's day.

As loud as thunder when she rocks out on her guitar.

As spooky as a cemetery at night-time.

As chilled out as a fridge-freezer.

As clever as a supercomputer.

As artistic as Van Gogh.

| Lincoln | Bobby | Lucy | Leni | Luna | Lisa |

2 Practise writing a few similes here. The first one has been done for you.

a. Lincoln is as excited as **a child on their birthday** when a plan goes well.

b. Lori is as happy as a _____ when she gets a call from Bobby.

c. Lily is as sad as a _____ when she has a full and smelly diaper.

d. Lynn is as disappointed as a _____ when she loses a competition.

e. Luan is as delighted as a _____ when people laugh at her jokes.

ALPHABETICAL ORDER

The Loud Family are having their family photograph taken and all the children need to stand in alphabetical order.

Alphabetical order is an ordering system whereby words are put into an order based on their first letter and that letter's position in the alphabet.

To order **b**ananas, **a**pples and **c**herries, we would look at each word's initial letter. Apples would be first as **a** is the first letter in the alphabet, bananas would be second and cherries third.

1

Put these characters into alphabetical order.

Clyde   Bobby   Lincoln

1.	
2.	
3.	

2

When there are words which start with the same letter, look at the <u>second</u> letter of the words to order them. Lana would come before Lola in alphabetic order as the second letter of Lana's name is an <u>a</u> which comes first in the alphabet.

Put these Loud family members into alphabetical order.

Lincoln   Luan   Lynn   Leni

1.	2.
3.	4.

3

When the first and second letters are the same, look at the <u>third</u> letter to indicate the alphabetical order.

Put these Loud family members into alphabetical order.

Lisa   Lily   Lincoln

1.
2.
3.

WORD FAMILIES

The Loud siblings all have the same roots and are related. They live in the same house, are part of the same family, even their names all start with the same letter!

Words also have families, these are groups of words with the same root word and related meanings.

Tip: Sometimes the word **base** is used instead of **root**. A base word is a root that also has meaning on its own, e.g., it is already a complete word.

Auto is a base word for a family of words such as automatic, automobile, automated. They have similar meanings.

1 Sort the words below into their families.

| tricycle | television | triangle | microscope | telescope |
| telephone | microphone | tripod | microwave | |

Family 1	Family 2	Family 3

2 Lincoln has worked out the meaning of the base word for each family. Can you draw lines to match the base words to their family meaning?

micro	distant
tri	small
tele	three

PREFIXES

Spade Nifty is a normal man but when he changes into Ace Savvy, Lincoln believes he becomes the world's greatest crime fighting superhero.

A **prefix** is a group of letters put in front of a root (or base) word. The prefix **super** makes Ace more than just a hero.

1

Circle the prefix on all of these words. The first one has been done for you.

supermarket	midnight	impossible	impolite
indoors	misplace	superstar	incomplete
superman	unusual	nonsense	unequal

2

Complete the chart.

Prefix	Root word	New word
super	man	
	write	rewrite
in	dependent	
im	mature	
	patient	impatient
super		superstar
non	sense	
	equal	unequal

DIRECT SPEECH

Luan loves to tell funny stories. To make sure she remembers them, she writes then down.

When speech is written down, it is called direct speech. Here is a reminder of our direct speech top tips:

Speech marks:
The words that are spoken are punctuated with inverted commas.

New speaker, new line:
Each time the speaker changes, you should start a new line to make it clear that a different person is speaking.

Reporting clause:
This is the writing that says who has spoken, there should be punctuation (a comma, question mark, exclamation mark etc.) between the direct speech and the reporting clause.

Inverted commas **go directly around the actual words being said by the character**. Punctuation, such as a question mark, is placed inside the inverted commas. Imagine a speech bubble – the inverted commas act like a speech bubble.

1 As usual, Luan is telling Lincoln some of her best jokes. Write the joke conversations below using inverted commas and the correct punctuation.

a. Luan asked, what did the teacher say to the cat about their handwriting?
i don't know sighed Lincoln
it's paw-fect! snorted Luan

b. What is sticky and brown? Luan giggled
I don't know, you tell me! Lincoln replied
A stick! Hahaha! laughed Luan

2 Rewrite Lincoln and Clyde's conversation into direct speech with inverted commas.
Top tip: Be sure to use interesting words instead of said!

I've got a great idea! Let's sneak around the back and wait for them there.

Excellent! I love it when a plan comes together.

READING COMPREHENSION

Lynn has written a report for the school newspaper. Read her sports report and answer the questions which follow.

1 Circle the correct answer.

a. How did the team get to the match?

Big car   Bus   Taxi

b. What was the weather?

Partly cloudy   Sunny   Dull

c. What didn't the supporters eat?

Hotdogs   Hamburgers   Nachos

d. How did some of Lynn's team feel?

Happy   Anxious   Excited

e. How did the team smell at the end?

Sweaty   Sweet   Stinky

ROYAL WOOD'S WINNING TEAM

By Lynn Loud

Yesterday, the Royal Woods Middle School baseball team were set to face their greatest baseball rivals. There was much cheering aboard the school bus on the way to Royal Woods Baseball Stadium. The sun was shining and excitement was in the air. The stands were full of supporters who munched on hot dogs and nachos with stinky cheese. Some of the team members were a bit anxious as our opponents looked big but I, Lynn Loud (never to be beaten), knew we'd succeed.

Royal Woods has a long record of having the best batters and catchers in the state due to raw skill and coach Keck's high standards. There is also the Royal Woods secret weapon: sheer determination to win! At one point, we were two runs down, but we did not accept defeat. We got three home runs to finish the game. The loyal Royal Woods supporters jumped out of their seats spilling their drinks, hotdogs and nachos all over the team with delight. Now the team smell like stinky cheese but we're very happy that we won.

2 Answer the following in a sentence or two.

a. Explain how the team reacted to being two runs down.

_____

_____

b. What did the supporters do when Lynn's team won?

_____

_____

CONJUNCTIONS

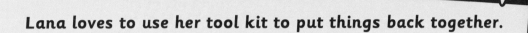

Lana loves to use her tool kit to put things back together.

Just like the superglue in Lana's toolbox, conjunctions are special words used to glue together two parts of a sentence, phrase or clause.

Common conjunctions include:

and	or	but	so	because	after
until	yet	if	when	since	while

Conjunctions can come at the start of the sentence or in the middle.

> **When** something is broken in the house, I like to get out my toolbox.

Here, the conjunction comes at the start of the sentence. There is a comma in the middle which separates the two clauses.

> I like to get out my toolbox **when** something is broken in the house.

Here, the sentence has been rewritten with the conjunction put in the middle.

---

1 Rewrite these sentences with the conjunction in the middle.

a. Before I go to bed, I always brush my teeth.

_____

b. After I tell a joke, everyone laughs.

_____

c. While I'm writing my poetry, everyone is always talking.

_____

---

2 From the table at the top of the page, choose a suitable conjunction to complete these sentences.

a. Lincoln and Clyde saw the next-door neighbour _____ looking through their telescope.

b. Lincoln and Clyde are a team who work together _____ their plan is complete.

c. Luan tells jokes and puns _____ everyone is entertained.

d. Luna often talks in song lyrics _____ she wants to be a rockstar.

SPELLING PATTERN -SION

Lisa is once again experimenting and mixing different potions together to see if she can make an explosion. The loud bang has blown the tiles off the roof!

> **-sion** can be a tricky word ending. If a word ending is pronounced "shun" then the spelling pattern will be **-sion**.
> **Top tip:** listen carefully as you say the words.

WARNING

RISK OF EXPLOSION

1

Put the **-sion** ending on the word beginnings and match them to the pictures.

colli-

televi-

explo-

illu-

confu-

vi-

-sion

a. _____

b. _____

c. _____

d. _____

e. _____

f. _____

2

Complete the sentences with a **-sion** word.

a. Let's watch _____ tonight.

b. Be careful as Lisa's experiment might cause an _____ .

c. Clyde's _____ is blurry without his glasses.

d. Lana and Lola banged heads in their _____ .

television

explosion

vision

collision

MAKING PREDICTIONS

The Loud children love to make predictions about what they think might happen next.

> A **prediction** is using what you already know about the people and situation to make a reasonable estimation of what might happen next.

1 Think about this situation: Lincoln and Clyde want to go to buy snacks from the store but they have no money. They have decided to do some odd jobs around the neighbourhood. They predict that this will earn them enough money for lots of snacks.

Can you write three alternative predictions of what could happen?

1. _____

2. _____

3. _____

2 Look at these pictures and predict what might happen next.

SPELLING TRICKY WORDS

Lucy's poetry contains some tricky words. The more she uses them, the easier it will be to remember how to spell them. Lincoln is helping her take a closer look.

1 Help Lincoln and Lucy use the letter clues in the crossword to insert the tricky words.

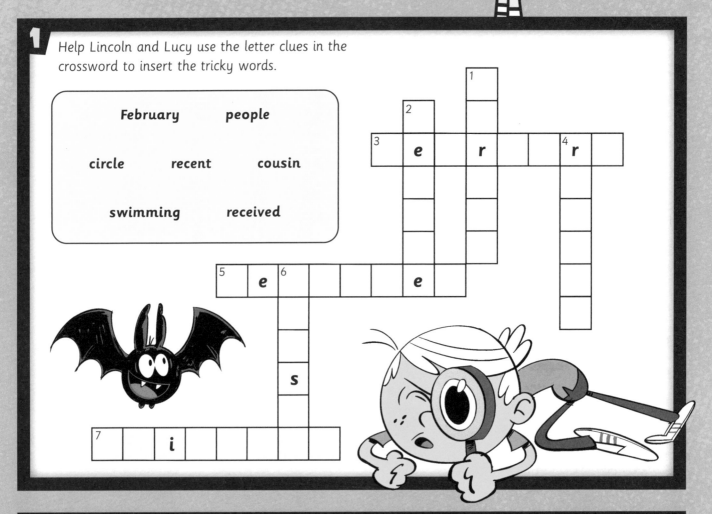

February   people

circle   recent   cousin

swimming   received

2 Use some of the words above to fill in the blanks in these sentences.

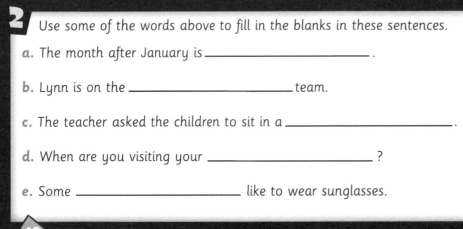

a. The month after January is _____ .

b. Lynn is on the _____ team.

c. The teacher asked the children to sit in a _____ .

d. When are you visiting your _____ ?

e. Some _____ like to wear sunglasses.

PREPOSITIONS

Cliff the cat can be quite mischievous. He has just eaten Lincoln's dinner and is now hiding behind the chair!

Behind shows the position of the cat in relation to the chair. The word **behind** is a **preposition**. A preposition shows how a noun or pronoun is related to another word in a sentence. Prepositions often relate to the location that something is in, like the example above.

1 Circle the **preposition** in each of these sentences.

a. The balloons flew above the house.

b. Lily is under the table.

c. Lincoln stood next to Clyde.

d. The boys parked their bikes between the trees.

e. Luna put her guitar inside the case.

2 Look at these words and identify the missing prepositions in the sentences.

beside	on	under	in	through

a. Lincoln is floating _____ the paddling pool.

b. Clyde is swinging _____ the monkey bars.

c. Lynn burst _____ the door.

d. Lana and Lola sat _____ each other.

e. Lori and Bobby had a picnic _____ the big tree.

19

PREFIX RE-

Bobby is hopelessly and utterly in love with Lori and wants to write her a special poem. He has found it very hard and keeps having to <u>revisit</u> his poem each day. He constantly <u>reviews</u> what he has written but can't <u>recall</u> what he wants to write.

Prefixes are groups of letters put in front of a root verb which will change the meaning of the word. The prefix **re-** means do again. **Re+write = rewrite**. Rewrite means to write again.

1

The prefix **re-** can be used in front of some verbs to make a new word but not all verbs make sense with a **re-** prefix. Sort these words into the correct column in the table. The first one has been done for you.

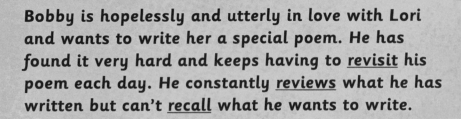

| rerun | ~~reeat~~ | return | redance | resleep | refish | replay | reheat |

Makes a new word	Does not make a new word
	reeat

2

Use the words below to fill in the blanks in these sentences.

reappeared

replayed

reheated

remade

retold

a. Leni _____ her outfit out of new fabric.

b. Luan _____ the same joke to all of the Loud children.

c. Luna _____ her new song over and over.

d. Lucy _____ from out of nowhere.

e. Lana _____ the dinner using the fire pit.

PREPOSITIONS

Lincoln lives next door to grumpy Mr. Grouse. He is always losing his balls when they go over the fence during a game of garden baseball. Lincoln has decided to sneak into Mr. Grouse's garden in the morning, before he wakes up, to collect up the balls.

> **Prepositions** are words that tell us **where (place)** or **when (time)** something is happening in relation to something else.

1

Complete the sentences below using the correct **time preposition**.

After	before	during	On Saturday afternoon	until

a. _____ , Lincoln and Clyde were throwing a ball about in the garden.

b. Lincoln and Clyde hit the ball too hard _____ their game of baseball.

c. The boys kept playing _____ they ran out of balls.

d. _____ Mr. Grouse picked up the stray balls, he hid them in his cupboard.

e. Lincoln snuck into Mr. Grouse's garden _____ the sun came up.

2

Sort these prepositions into time and place. Colour in **prepositions of place** (where) in red and **prepositions of time** (when) in blue.

on Monday	later	after
beyond	underneath	during
beside	before	next to

3

Read the sentences and circle the type of preposition which is used.

a. It's been just minutes since Lily's last stinky diaper bomb. TIME / PLACE

b. Lisa closed her bedroom door before she began her experiment. TIME / PLACE

c. Lynn threw her favourite baseball over the garden fence. TIME / PLACE

d. Lana peered under the car bonnet to check the problem. TIME / PLACE

SUFFIX -LY

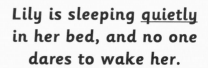

When Lily is sleeping <u>quietly</u>, the family know they must walk <u>gently</u>, not speak <u>loudly</u> and behave <u>calmly</u> in the house so they don't wake her.

A suffix is a group of letters put on the end of a word. Adding the suffix **-ly** to a word changes it from an adjective to an adverb. An **adverb** describes how an action is done.

Lily is sleeping <u>quietly</u> in her bed, and no one dares to wake her.

quiet + ly = quietly

1

Change these adjectives into adverbs by adding the –ly suffix. The first one has been done for you.

adjective	adverb
brave	bravely
quiet	
calm	
bold	
exact	
glad	

2

Have a look what happens when the word ends in y or e, and you add the -ly suffix.

happy
happy + ly = happily

gentle
gentle + ly = gently

Explain what happens.
<u>Hint:</u> Notice what happened to the letter y on the end of happy.

3

Use the following adverbs in a sentence.

calmly _____

happily _____

gently _____

PLOT LINES

Rita and Lynn Sr. have purchased some new Christmas decorations. Clyde has come over to help Lincoln with the decorating but Leni has spotted the new decorations and has her own ideas! She thinks they would make a marvellous new dress.

Plot lines for stories have elements which see the story build up to a problem, the problem is then solved and is followed by an ending. Have a look at the Loud House situation below and plot out the story.

1 How are Lincoln and Clyde going to keep the decorations away from Leni and get the house decorated? Could they distract Leni with something else?

Story start	Build up	Challenge and problem	The problem solved	Ending/ resolution
Mum and Dad have bought new Christmas decorations.	Clyde has come over to help Lincoln with the decorating.			

2 Use your plan to write your story. Make sure you use plenty of description so that the reader gets a clear picture of what is happening and you create a sense of atmosphere. Continue on a piece of paper if you run out of space.

WRITING PRACTICE

Luna wants to write out a copy of her new lyrics to give to Sam Sharp, her band mate and friend. She knows her handwriting needs to be super neat!

> Handwriting should be neat and consistent in size. All ascending letters should be the same height and all descending letters should be the same length.

1 Can you help Luna write out the lyrics below in your best handwriting?

> I've got stars in my eyes and a guitar in my hand.
>
> I rock out whenever I can.
>
> It's my song that really rocks. I've got rocks in my socks.
>
> I've got stars in my eyes and a guitar in my hand.
>
> I'm a real rockstar and we're about to jam.

_____

_____

_____

_____

_____

_____

_____

_____

_____

_____

2 Luna is struggling to think of a suitable title for her song. What do you think her song could be called? Write a title neatly below.

_____

PAST PERFECT TENSE

Lana has been busy fixing her dad's car as he couldn't get the engine to start. After five minutes under the bonnet, she shouted, "I have finished!"

When shouting this, Lana used the **past perfect tense**. The past perfect tense uses **has** or **have** to show that something has happened but is still relevant now. For example – I **have painted** the room.

1 Complete these past perfect sentences by adding in a past tense verb. Choose the correct verb from the list. The first one has been done for you.

~~walk~~

cook

wash

talk

cycle

a. "I have **walk<u>ed</u>** the dog," said Leni.

b. Bobby and Lori have _____ on the phone.

c. Lincoln and Clyde have _____ on their bikes.

d. Luan has _____ the car.

e. Lincoln has _____ the dinner.

2 Lana was given a list of jobs to do around the house. She couldn't wait to get started and get her hands dirty! Write a diary entry for Lana detailing the tasks she did that day using the past perfect tense. It has already been started for you.

- **Downstairs loo needs plunging**
- **Pond needs cleaning**
- **Grass needs mowing**
- **Lola's hairdryer needs fixing**
- **Lily's cot needs painting**

I have worked hard fixing a lot of broken things around the house. I have started by working on Dad's car.

READING COMPREHENSION

Lana and Lola have been in the kitchen all day helping their dad bake up some sweet treats to feed the family.

Read what they have been up to and answer the questions below. To answer these questions, you will need to use inference. This means you will need to use the clues and evidence in the text to form your thinking for your answers.

1 Why was Lana washing up the bowls and beaters? Tick the correct answer.

a. Because the bowl and beaters were broken. ☐

b. Because washing up is her favourite hobby. ☐

c. Because they used them in the baking so they were dirty. ☐

Lana was still wearing a chef's hat while she was washing up the bowls and beaters. Lola waited impatiently with tubes of pink icing and sparkly sprinkles at the ready. The sweet smell of cinnamon wafted out of the hot oven. Lola wore an apron with pink ruffles, whilst Lana opted for fresh overalls. Both were smeared with batter.

When the washing up was complete, they got out some cooling racks and the oven mitts. When the timer went off, they eagerly called for their dad to come and help them as they knew they shouldn't take hot things out of the oven by themselves. As Lincoln and Clyde walked through the kitchen a few minutes later and saw the cookies on the side, they smiled at each other. "We've arrived at just the right time," Lincoln thought happily.

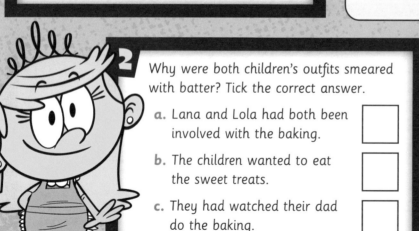

2 Why were both children's outfits smeared with batter? Tick the correct answer.

a. Lana and Lola had both been involved with the baking. ☐

b. The children wanted to eat the sweet treats. ☐

c. They had watched their dad do the baking. ☐

3 How was Lola feeling? Tick the correct answer.

a. Excited ☐

b. Anxious ☐

c. Impatient ☐

4 Explain why she was feeling that way. Use evidence from the story to support your answer.

_____

HANDWRITING

Lucy likes to write poetry and has written a poem about one of her favourite things - ghosts coming out at night.

When handwriting, some letters are joined using a diagonal stroke such as ck and some are joined with a horizontal stroke such as oo.

Some letters are best left un-joined. These include capital letters which start sentences and names.

1 Help Lucy make her poem presentable by copying it out in joined up handwriting.

Lucy's Poem
When all is dark and there is no sun,
We all come out and people run.
Ghosts are moving all about,
If you see one just give a shout.
When night is over and all is done,
Tomorrow night there will be more fun.

2 Extend Lucy's poem by adding some more lines. Remember that capital letters are not joined to the others.

PREFIXES MIS- AND DIS-

After watching a magic show, Lincoln and Clyde have been inspired to work on a magic trick of their own, the ability to change the meaning of words.

Adding **prefixes** to the beginning of words changes their meaning. Adding the prefix **dis-** or **mis-** to a word will create a negative meaning, often the opposite of what it meant before.

In Clyde and Lincoln's trick, they first made a bunch of flowers **appear**. But then, using their prefix trick, adding the prefix **dis-** made the flowers **disappear**.

dis + appear = disappear

1 Which of the prefixes needs to be added to give the word the opposite meaning? Draw a line from the prefix to the correct root word. The first one has been done for you.

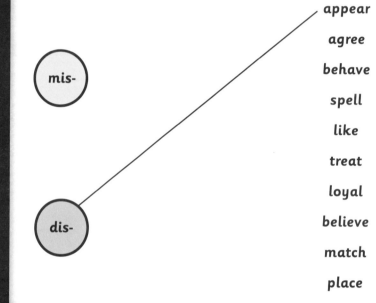

mis-

dis-

appear
agree
behave
spell
like
treat
loyal
believe
match
place

2 Lincoln and Clyde have performed their 'prefix trick' and come up with the following words. Can you use each word in a sentence? The first one has been done for you.

mismatch   Leni found two gloves but they were a **mismatch**.

disagree   _____

misbehave   _____

dislike   _____

misplace   _____

PRONOUNS AND NOUNS

Lincoln has brought home the class spider, Frank.

"He is terrifying!" shrieked Leni.

"No, he's not, he's fascinating!" grinned Lucy.

"Actually, '_he's_' not terrifying or fascinating, he is a '_she_'!" chuckled Lincoln, after discovering Frank's babies and realising that Frank was actually a female.

"She is a wonderful spider!" replied Lucy.

Nouns are words for people, places and things. **Pronouns** replace nouns to add variety and avoid repetition within a sentence. For example, instead of always using the noun **Lincoln**, you could use the pronoun **he** in some sentences.

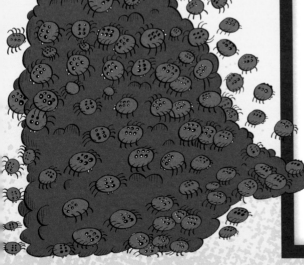

1

Sort the nouns and the pronouns below. Note: some pronouns are plural like 'they.'

Lincoln	he	they	we
spider	Luan	Lucy	yours
Clyde	myself	baby	

Nouns	Pronouns

2

Rewrite the sentence and change the underlined noun to a pronoun. The first one has been done for you.

a.	Bobby was going to be late to meet Lori and **Bobby** didn't want to make her wait.	Bobby was going to be late to meet Lori and **he** didn't want to make her wait.
b.	Leni was designing a new outfit and **Leni** was very excited.	
c.	Lynn wants to make a new team so **Lynn** can play football after school.	

CREATIVE WRITING

The theatre group has been set a task of writing a new script. Luan knows that writing a script is very different to writing a story.

Scripts use a **narrator**, put the **speakers on the left**, contain **no speech marks** and stage directions are written in **brackets**.

1 Luan has decided to write a script about her brother, Lincoln, and his friend Clyde. Have a look at her script so far. Draw a line from the script element to where it is in the script.

Use of narrator

Speakers on the left

Stage directions in brackets

Narrator: It is a sunny day without a cloud in the sky. Lincoln and Clyde are under a tree thinking.

Lincoln: What should we do today? It's just so hot. (Lincoln pulls a fan out of his pocket and fans himself.)

Clyde: I think we should just stay in the shade and keep cool.

Lincoln: I've got it. I know what we should do. (Lincoln looks excited.)

2 Think carefully about what Luan might write next. What could Lincoln's amazing idea be? Carry on the script using the template below.

Character's name or narrator	What the character/narrator says and what the character does (written in brackets)

EXPANDED NOUN PHRASES

There is a strange smell in the Loud house. Uh oh, there is a diaper on the floor again. In fact, <u>there is a dirty, rancid diaper steaming on the floor</u>. Eww!

The second description is a bit more gross isn't it? That's because it's giving a bit more detail with an **expanded noun phrase**.

Expanded noun phases are phrases which **include an adjective or two to describe the noun**. For example, Lily's diaper versus Lily's **dirty, rancid** diaper. Dirty and rancid gives us more detail about the type of diaper it is.

Expanded noun phrases can also **tell us where the noun is**. For example, The diaper is **steaming on the floor**.

Expanded noun phrases help the reader to develop a clear picture in their head of what is written.

1 Underline the **adjectives** in these phrases. The first one has been done for you.

a. Lori has a <u>shiny, new</u> phone.

b. Leni's new, sparkly dress fits her perfectly.

c. Lisa's test tube is full of green, smelly smoke.

d. Lucy's dark, gloomy poem silenced everyone.

e. Lana wants a long, green snake as a pet.

f. Lola spilt the sparkly, pink glitter everywhere.

2 Underline the additional information about **where the noun is** in these sentences.

a. The complicated experiment is bubbling <u>in the lab</u>.

b. Luan has hidden a bulging whoopee cushion underneath the sofa cushions.

c. Lynn was dusting her shiny, precious trophies on the mantel piece.

d. The battered, scuffed wheels on the skateboard spun round.

e. Bobby's delicious pizza bubbled away as it baked in the pizza oven.

f. At the pageant, Lola marched her glittering shoes down the catwalk.

PARTS OF A SENTENCE

Despite being twins, Lana and Lola are very different. But the differences in their personalities and skills can be a great help when they team up.

Just like the twins, words have differences too. **Nouns** are people, places and things. **Verbs** are action words. **Prepositions** are words that tell someone where or when something is in relation to something else. **Adjectives** are used to describe a noun and **adverbs** are used to describe a verb (how an action is done). When these different word types are put together, they make a successful

1

Look at the words below. Lola is looking for the **nouns** - circle them in red. Lana is looking for **verbs** - circle the verbs in blue.

diamond ring	running	sit	singing	dreaming
tiara	dribbling	jump	sleeping	
yawning	shoes	lollypop	sequins	cake

2

Help Lana and Lola to sort these **adjectives** and **adverbs** into their correct boxes. Draw a line from each word to its correct box.

quietly

quickly

pretty

pink

slowly

long

adverb

adjective

3

Circle the correct **preposition** in the sentences below. The first one has been done for you.

a. Clyde is <u>on</u> / (in) the Loud house.

b. The baseball is always flying over / in the fence.

c. Lily is sitting in / over a sticky diaper.

d. Lisa's experiment is on / between the table.

e. Bobby messaged Lori during / between his break.

f. Leni has been looking for her sunglasses on / since Tuesday.

SPELLING PATTERN -TION

When Lynn looks at the team <u>selection</u> and sees her name, she smiles and is ready for <u>action</u>. During the game, she gives her full <u>attention</u> so she can play to <u>perfection</u>. She knows that the only <u>position</u> she will be happy with in the ice hockey league is first place... there is no other <u>option</u>!

The spelling pattern **-tion** is easy. It is used to form a **noun** which means the action or result of a **verb**.

reflect	reflect + tion = reflection

Reflect is a verb (an action word) but adding the suffix **-tion** makes it a noun. Root words which end in **t** or **te** will usually be expanded with the **-tion** spelling pattern. The **t** or **te** is taken away, and the suffix **-tion** is added.

---

1 Expand these words with the **-tion** spelling pattern. The first one has been done for you.

Root word	Expanded word with -tion spelling pattern
act	action
animate	
donate	
disrupt	
instruct	
affect	
select	
rotate	

2 Add the correct **-tion** word for each sentence.

> eruption   addition   station
> invitation   injection

a. Bobby was sad to wave Lori goodbye at the train _____ .

b. Lincoln has already completed his _____ maths homework.

c. Clyde wants to give Lori an _____ to his party.

d. The nurse gave Lily an _____ .

e. Lisa's model volcano has not had an _____ yet.

EDITING AND CORRECTING

Lucy is writing a report on vampires. Lisa's told her she should check it for mistakes before she hands it in at school.

Once a piece of work has been completed, it is important to check punctuation, sentence structure and use of description. There is usually always something which can be changed to make it even better!

Take a look at Lucy's report on vampires.

Vampires

Vampires are a type of monster. vampires cannot go out in sunlight and sleep during

daylight. Vampires have two fangs. garlic and silver can weaken a vampire Vampires

can disappear when they click their fingers. Vampires do not produce a reflection in

mirrors glass or other objects. Not many people believe in Vampires. I do

1 Help Lucy to edit her report. Use the list below to help you check the text and add in any edits that are needed.

Item	Checked or corrected
Capital letters: Sentences and proper nouns such as names start with a capital letter.	
Punctuation: Every sentence ends with a full stop and there are commas in a list. Questions have question marks.	
Sentence structure: There are longer complex sentences and shorter ones too. Can you join any sentences together to create a range of sentence lengths?	
Pronouns are used so that nouns are not repeated. Can you say something else instead of vampires all the time?	
Description: There are plenty of adjectives to interest the reader.	

PARAGRAPHS AND HEADINGS

Clyde and Lincoln are writing a report about bees for a project at school. They enjoyed doing the research but now they've reached the tricky part of writing it up in a proper, organised report with paragraphs and sub-headings.

Paragraphs are used to describe or explain an idea. New paragraphs are marked by starting a new line and are required when there is a change in theme. They make writing easier to read. In non-fiction writing, the paragraphs usually have **sub-headings**, which introduce what the next section of writing is about.

2 The paragraphs have one main idea each. Read the statements below and decide if they are true or false.

a. Paragraph 1 is about the job of the worker bees.

   True / False

b. Paragraph 2 is about the job of the Queen bee.

   True / False

c. Paragraph 3 is about the uses of honey.

   True / False

d. Paragraph 4 is about the job of the drones.

   True / False

1 Help Clyde and Lincoln by writing suitable sub-headings for their paragraphs. **Top tip:** Often a sub-heading is in the form of a question which will be answered in the paragraph that follows.

Bees

Bees live in a house called a hive. It is a very busy place. Each hive has three types of bees who live there. These bees include the Queen bee, the worker bees and the drones.

The most important bee in the hive is the Queen bee. There is only one Queen bee in a hive. If the Queen bee is lost or passes away, the other bees will stop working. The Queen's job is to lay the eggs.

The worker bees have a variety of jobs. They build cells for the baby bees and look after them. They also keep the hive clean. They go out and collect pollen which they turn into honey.

Drone bees have only one job. They mate with the Queen.

READING COMPREHENSION

You'll need to look for clues like a detective to complete the activities on this page.

Lori was stomping around the house, huffing and puffing. "Where is my phone?" she grumbled as she slammed her bedroom door hard.

Even though she hadn't said it in so many words, Lincoln could read the clues to tell that his sister was in a very bad mood! Lincoln had used **inference** to judge his sister's mood; he had seen the signs and worked it out!

Carefully read the paragraphs opposite. It contains clues which indicate what is about to happen but it doesn't tell us EXACTLY what is going to happen. When you are reading, think about how the characters are feeling and acting. Use the clues and what you know to answer the questions. This is called **inference**.

Lincoln woke up super early. The sun was just peaking over the horizon. He texted Clyde right away to make sure he was awake too. He was. Lincoln wanted to jump on the bed but knew he shouldn't. He ran downstairs to quickly eat his breakfast.

Quick as a flash, Lincoln put on his best suit and the shiny shoes his Grandpa had given him. They were a bit too big but he wore them anyway. Lincoln put on his smart, red tie. He thought his suit itched a bit but that was okay. Lincoln and Clyde walked briskly to school. The fabric on Clyde's suit sparkled a bit in the morning sunshine. It was going to be a great day, Lincoln thought. A day that he and Clyde would remember for the rest of their lives! Perhaps they would even have their pictures in the newspaper.

They helped prepare the school stage for their special guest. They set up the podium, microphone and the speaker on stage. They rolled out the red carpet at the front of the school and waited eagerly to see the arrival of the stretch limousine. The other children started to arrive at school, chatting excitedly. Lincoln's fingers shivered just a little in anticipation of who he was about to meet.

1 Use **inference** to answer these questions.

a. How was Lincoln feeling on that morning? Give examples of the actions which tell us he was feeling that way.

_____

_____

b. After the special guest arrives at the school, they will be doing something on the stage. What might they do? How do you know.

_____

_____

c. Why do you think Lincoln put on his best suit?

_____

_____

DIRECT SPEECH

Luan knows that her family could be excellent content for her new stand-up comedy routine! She's been sat listening to the rants and rumblings of her siblings and has been writing notes in her notebook.

As we learnt before, inverted commas or speech marks surround direct speech. They **go directly around the actual words being said by the character**. Punctuation, such as a question mark, is placed inside the inverted commas. Imagine a speech bubble - the inverted commas act like a speech bubble.

1 Identify if Luan's sentences are punctuated correctly.

a. "Where are my trainers?" asked Lincoln.   correct / incorrect

b. Lily's diaper needs changing again! "yelled Lana."   correct / incorrect

c. "I have another new job," exclaimed Bobby.   correct / incorrect

d. "I've got awesome, new lyrics for a song, declared" Luna   correct / incorrect

e. "I literally don't know what to wear!! Moaned Lori."   correct / incorrect

2 Rewrite the incorrectly punctuated sentences above next to the character who said them. Remember to add in the inverted commas and any other missed punctuation.

a._____

b._____

c._____

PLURALS AND POSSESSIVES

Clyde likes to feed his cats treats and play silly games with them.

As we know, a noun is a person, place or thing. Adding an **s** to a noun will make it **plural**. This means there are more than one.

cat

cats

Adding an **apostrophe** and an **s** to a noun means something belongs to the noun. This is called **possessive**.

The **cat's collar** is blue. The collar belongs to the cat.

---

1 Look at the sentences. Circle to indicate if the **s** is used to make the noun a **plural** or a **possessive**.

a. **Lori's** phone is low on battery.   plural / possessive

b. Lincoln has lots and lots of **sisters**.   plural / possessive

c. The hamster has lots of **toys**.   plural / possessive

d. **Lincoln's** drink is smooth and delicious.   plural / possessive

e. **Leni's** sunglasses are lost in the Loud house.   plural / possessive

---

2 Can you help Clyde and Lincoln to write a sentence for each of these nouns?
The first one has been done for you.

| a. Tree | tree's (possessive) | The tree's leaves are turning brown. |
| | trees (plural) | There are plenty of trees near the Loud house. |

| b. Pencil | pencil's (possessive) | |
| | pencils (plural) | |

PLURAL APOSTROPHES

Lisa has agreed to help Lucy create a spooky potion! Lucy has written a list of unusual ingredients they will need, but Lisa is a bit confused by some of the items on the list, due to Lucy's use of possessive apostrophes.

Possessive apostrophes can be a bit tricky if the noun is plural. **Plural** means when there is more than one.

If the owner noun is plural and **ends in s**, just add an apostrophe. For example, the wings which belong to the swarm of locusts would be the **locusts' wings**.

However, if the owner noun is plural and **does not end in s**, you add the apostrophe and the s. For example, toenails which belong to children (plural of child) would be the **children's toenails**.

---

1 Complete Lucy's ingredients list using the correct possessive apostrophe. The first one has been done for you.

a.	hats belonging to a group of witches	witches' hats
b.	legs belonging to a group of frogs	
c.	stools belonging to a group of fairies	
d.	eyes belonging to a group of newts	

---

2 Rewrite the phrases below using a possessive apostrophe. The first one has been done for you.

a.	hair belonging to people	people's hair
b.	fleece belonging to sheep	
c.	feathers belonging to geese	
d.	earwax belonging to children	

FRONTED ADVERBIALS

Lori spends so much of her day messaging Bobby and she wants to make sure her sentences are making her sound super smart! Lisa has told her all about adverbials.

Adverbials are words or phrases which describe or give more information about the action in the sentence. They can describe **how**, **when** or **where** something happened. **Fronted adverbials** are adverbials found at the start of the sentence and are punctuated with a comma afterwards.

Lincoln visited Grandpa **yesterday**.

Yesterday is the adverbial. It explains **when** the visit took place. The same sentence could be written with the adverbial at the start of the sentence. For example, **Yesterday**, Lincoln visited Grandpa.

1 Rewrite Lori's sentences to Bobby with the adverbial at the front.
HINT: Remember to add a comma!

a. Lana and Lola decorated their room last weekend.

_____

b. Leni is trying to do her homework upstairs.

_____

c. Lincoln crashed his skateboard three times.

_____

d. Lucy's lunch disappeared mysteriously.

_____

2 Lori was texting so quickly that she forgot to add the commas after the fronted adverbial. Put the commas in the correct place in the sentences below.

a. Early in the morning all was quiet in the house.

b. Frantically Clyde tried to mop up his nosebleed.

c. In the blink of an eye Leni snatched a dress from my wardrobe.

POINT OF VIEW

Lisa is used to sharing her point of view, especially as she is most certainly the smartest of the Loud bunch!

The point of view in writing tells us about the perspective from which the story is being told. There are usually three viewpoints: **first person**, **second person** and **third person**.

Stories written in **first person** are told from the perspective of the character and use words such as I, me and we. Text written in **second person** involves the author addressing the reader. This is done using words like you, your and yours. In **third person**, the author acts as the narrator using the characters' names, he, she and they.

1 Rewrite these sentences about the siblings into first person.

a.

Third person:
Lori is the oldest.

First person:

b.

Third person:
Lynn's team won.

First person:

c.

Third person:
Lisa and Lily are the youngest.

First person:

2 As usual, Lisa is busy in her laboratory. Look at the event below and rewrite it in first person.
Top tip: Pretend you are Lisa when you're writing.

Lisa has created a new substance which removes sticky gum from any surface. It took 27 tries for Lisa to perfect the substance. She is excited to tell everyone about her incredible discovery.

_____

_____

_____

_____

_____

_____

READING COMPREHENSION

Mrs. Johnson has written a short description of the Loud family to remind her of who is in the family. There really are so many siblings to remember! Have a read of what she has written and answer the questions below.

The Loud Family

The Loud family is large. It consists of Mum and Dad and eleven children. It can be complete chaos at times with so many people living in one house.

There are ten girls and one boy. The boy's name is Lincoln and he is the middle child. Lori, Leni, Luna, Luan and Lynn are older than Lincoln. Lucy, Lana, Lola, Lisa and Lily are younger than Lincoln. Lily is a baby; she is just 15 months old. For the most part, the children get along and help each other out.

There are also a few pets, including Charles the dog and Cliff the cat. There is also a yellow canary who lives there called Walt, and a hamster called Geo. Geo is a clever hamster who can follow commands.

1 Circle the correct answer.

a. How many children are in the Loud family?

ten   eleven   twelve

b. Who is the youngest child?

Lisa   Lily   Lincoln

c. Lincoln is...

the youngest

the middle child

the oldest

2 Use your opinion to answer these questions.

a. Is the Loud family a big family? Explain why you think that.

_____

b. Is it difficult for Lincoln to be the only boy within the family? Explain.

_____

c. The house can be complete chaos. Explain.

_____

3 Use inference (clues from the text and what you already know) to answer the following questions.

a. Is it often noisy in the house? Explain.

_____

_____

b. Can you tell from the text whether the children get on well together? Explain.

_____

_____

SPELLING TRICKY WORDS

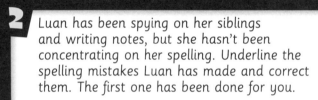

Spelling is something that many of the Loud children struggle with! They know that some words are tricky to spell. The more you use them, the more you will remember how to spell them.

1
Begin by circling the correct spelling of the words below:

a.	grammar	**or**	grammer
b.	axcident	**or**	accident
c.	sentanse	**or**	sentence
d.	reign	**or**	reegn
e.	February	**or**	Februry
f.	ayth	**or**	eighth
g.	naughty	**or**	nawghty
h.	library	**or**	librery
i.	knowledge	**or**	nowlidge

2
Luan has been spying on her siblings and writing notes, but she hasn't been concentrating on her spelling. Underline the spelling mistakes Luan has made and correct them. The first one has been done for you.

a. Lincoln is getting ready for his <u>Grammer</u> test.

Grammar
_____

b. It sounds like Lisa may have had an axcident with an experiment.

_____

c. Leni is heading to the librery to read up on clothes making.

_____

d. Bobby is talking nervously about the new job he starts in Februry.

_____

3
Uh oh – Luan wasn't concentrating again and accidentally let off her squirty flower all over her notebook! The water has rubbed out some of the words. Help her to fill in the blanks.

a. gra _ _ _ r

b. e _ _ hth

c. s _ nten _ _

d. r _ _ gn

e. Feb _ _ ary

f. n _ _ ght _

g. kn _ _ le _ _ _

h. lib _ a _ _

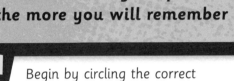

43

CINQUAIN POETRY

Luna is learning how to write Cinquain poems so she can use the format for a new song.

Lucy
Dark and spooky
Reading scaring hiding
Appearing out of the shadows
Poet

Cinquain poems only have five lines, but each line has a particular number of syllables.

Line 1	Two syllables (which is also the title)
Line 2	Four syllables
Line 3	Six syllables (often ending in **ing**)
Line 4	Eight syllables
Line 5	Two syllables

Lynn Loud
Sporty sister
Running jumping scoring
On the sports team always winning
Athlete

1

Can you help Luna write a Cinquain poem about another of her siblings?

Line 1	Two syllables (which is also the title)	
Line 2	Four syllables	
Line 3	Six syllables (often ending in ing)	
Line 4	Eight syllables	
Line 5	Two syllables	

2

Write out your poem in neat handwriting.

_____

_____

_____

_____

_____

FRONTED ADVERBIALS

Lynn is super competitive, and when it comes to sport, she makes sure she always comes first.

Just like Lynn, fronted adverbials always come first! They belong at the start of the sentence and give information about the verb in the sentence.

Fronted adverbial + comma + main clause

As we know, fronted adverbials can describe **time** (when something happened), **manner** (how something happened) or **place** (where something happened).

1 Add these frontal adverbials into the chart to show what they are describing. It could be time, manner or place.

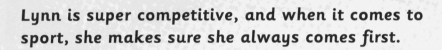

| Next year | Without warning | As fast as he could | Back at the house |
| After a while | On the street | Awkwardly | Far away | On Saturday |

Time – when	Manner - how	Place - where
Every Monday	Slowly	In Lincoln's room
During the afternoon	Carefully	Under the stairs
When I wake up	Baffled and confused	In the garden

When using a fronted adverbial at the beginning of a sentence, it must always be followed by a comma.

2 Look at these sentences with fronted adverbials.
Circle whether the comma is in the correct place or not.

a. On Monday, afternoon Lincoln and Clyde are putting their plan into action.　　correct / incorrect

b. Carefully, Lisa experimented until she found the perfect solution.　　correct / incorrect

c. Quick as a flash, Lincoln jumped into action.　　correct / incorrect

d. Unexpectedly there was, a knock on the door.　　correct / incorrect

ANSWERS

Page 2: Parts of a sentence

1. **Nouns:** ball, tongue, telephone, liquid, spider, sunglasses, baby rattle, guitar, test tube, Lincoln, door, hat
   Verbs: reading, pointing, pranking, running, yelling, chatting, catching, playing

2. large, pretty, rock, silly, smelly

3. **The chosen word should describe the verb. Examples could include:**
   a. Luan plays the guitar loudly.
   b. Lynn loves to play sports competitively.
   c. Leni always dresses beautifully.
   d. Lisa quietly works on her experiment.

Page 3: Handwriting practice

1 & 2. Accept any handwriting where the ascenders and descenders do not touch and are spaced appropriately.

Page 4: Homophones and Near Homophones

1. pear — pair
   meat — meet
   ball — bawl
   break — brake
   great — grate
   herd — heard
   knight — night
   blue — blew

2. a. meet   c. blew   e. heard
   b. missed   d. great

3. quiet — quite
   were — where
   further — father
   except — accept
   bury — berry

Page 5: Reading comprehension

1. a. false   c. true   e. true
   b. false   d. true   f. true

2. a. An answer which refers to cardboard, fabric and glass or crystal.
   b. An answer which refers to Lincoln and Lynn Sr.
   c. An answer which explains that Lynn Sr. was wondering where the tablecloth was so Leni knew she should return it.

Page 6: Direct speech

1. a. "Where's Cliff the cat?" asked Mum.
   b. "I love you, Lori!" swooned Bobby.
   c. "I'm a rock star," shouted Luna.
   d. "Who broke the car?" yelled Lynn Sn.
   e. "I love it when a prank comes together!" laughed Luan.

2. Accept any words which have the same or similar meaning to said.

Page 7: Indefinite articles

1. A list with 6 of the following:
   a skateboard, a diaper, an umbrella, a book, a bowl, a jar, an aeroplane toy, a football, a handbag, a guitar, an eggbox, a vase of flowers, a clock, an apron.

2. a. an x-ray   c. a uniform
   b. an honour   d. an hour

Page 8: Spelling pattern -cian

1. a. optician   d. magician
   b. physician   e. electrician
   c. musician   f. beautician

2. a. politician   c. technician
   b. mathematician   d. dietician

Page 9: Similes

1. Lincoln - As calm as the sea on a Summer's day.
   Bobby - As chilled out as a fridge-freezer.
   Lucy - As spooky as a cemetery at night-time.
   Leni - As artistic as Van Gogh.
   Luna - As loud as thunder as she rocks out on her guitar.
   Lisa - As clever as a supercomputer.

2. Any suitable similes which make sense in the sentence.

Page 10: Alphabetical order

1. Bobby, Clyde, Lincoln
2. Leni, Lincoln, Luan, Lynn
3. Lily, Lincoln, Lisa

Page 11: Word families

1. Family 1: tricycle, tripod, triangle
   Family 2: television, telescope, telephone
   Family 3: microscope, microphone, microwave

2. micro — small   tri — three
   tele — distant

Page 12: Prefixes

1. **super**market   **mid**night
   impossible   **im**polite
   indoors   **mis**place
   superstar   **in**complete
   superman   **un**usual
   nonsense   **un**equal

2. super – man – **superman**
   re – write – rewrite
   in – dependent – **independent**
   im – mature – **immature**
   im – patient – impatient
   super – **star** – superstar
   non – sense – **nonsense**
   un – equal – unequal

Page 13: Direct speech

1. a. Luan asked, "What did the teacher say to the cat about his handwriting?"
   "I don't know," sighed Lincoln.
   "It's paw-fect!" snorted Luan.
   b. "What is sticky and brown?" Luan giggled.
   "I don't know, you tell me!" Lincoln replied.
   "A stick! Hahaha!" laughed Luan.

2. "I've got a great idea! Let's sneak around the back and wait for them there," whispered Lincoln.

   "Excellent! I love it when a plan comes together." chuckled Clyde.

Page 14: Reading comprehension

1. a. bus   c. hamburgers   e. stinky
   b. sunny   d. anxious

2. a. Any suitable answer which explains the team would not give up or be defeated.
   b. Any suitable answer which explains that the supporters jumped up and spilt their foods and drinks.

Page 15: Conjunctions

1. a. I always brush my teeth before I go to bed.
   b. Everyone laughs after I tell a joke.
   c. Everyone is always talking while I'm writing my poetry

2. a. when / while   c. so / and
   b. until   d. because

Page 16: Spelling pattern -sion

1. a. television   d. vision
    b. collision   e. confusion
    c. explosion   f. illusion

2. a. television   c. vision
    b. explosion   d. collision

Page 17: Making predictions

1. Any alternative predictions that relate to Lincoln and Clyde such as, 'I predict that Lincoln and Clyde don't make any money' or 'I predict that it will be harder work than they think.'

2. Any predictions related to the images.

Page 18: Spelling tricky words

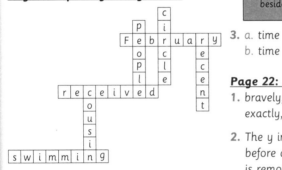

2. a. February   d. cousin
    b. swimming   e. people
    c. circle

Page 19: Prepositions

1. a. The balloons flew **above** the house.
    b. Lily is **under** the table.
    c. Lincoln stood **next to** Clyde.
    d. The boys parked their bikes **between** the trees.
    e. Luna put her guitar **inside** the case.

2. a. Lincoln is floating in the paddling pool.
    b. Clyde is swinging on the monkey bars.
    c. Lynn burst through the door.
    d. Lana and Lola sat beside each other.
    e. Lori and Bobby had a picnic under the big tree.

Page 20: Prefix re-

1. Makes new words:
rerun, return, replay, reheat
Does not makes new words:
reeat, redance, resleep, reeat

2. a. Leni remade her outfit out of new fabric.
    b. Luan retold the same joke to all of the Loud children.

c. Luna replayed her new song over and over.
d. Lucy reappeared from out of nowhere.
e. Lana reheated the dinner using the fire pit.

Page 21: Prepositions

1. a. On Saturday afternoon
    b. during
    c. until
    d. After
    e. before

2.

on Monday	later	after
beyond	underneath	during
beside	before	next to

3. a. time   c. place
    b. time   d. place

Page 22: Suffix -ly

1. bravely, quietly, calmly, boldly, exactly, gladly

2. The y in happy changes to an i before adding -ly and the e in gentle is removed before adding -ly.

3. Accept any sentences which make sense and include the adverbs.

Page 23: Plot lines

1. Table filled in with plausible ideas.

2. Story plotted with sufficient detail to keep the reader engaged.

Page 24: Writing practice

1. Accept neat joined up handwriting which is consistent in size and formation.

2. Accept a title. Capitals not joined but lower case letters joined.

Page 25: Past perfect tense

1. a. walked   c. washed
    b. talked   d. cooked
    c. cycled

2. Accept any sentences with past perfect tense.

Page 26: Reading comprehension

1. The correct answer is c
2. The correct answer is a
3. The correct answer is c
4. A written answer which explains why Lola was feeling impatient due to the fact she wanted to ice and sprinkle the sweet treats but they were still baking in the oven.

Page 27: Handwriting

1 & 2. Accept handwriting where capitals stand alone and other letters are appropriately joined with either a diagonal or horizontal stroke.

Page 28: Prefixes mis- and dis-

1. dis: disappear, disagree, dislike, disloyal, disbelieve
mis: misbehave, mistreat, mismatch, misspell, misplace

2. Accept any suitable sentences containing the given words.

Page 29: Pronouns and nouns

1. nouns: Lincoln, spider, Clyde, Luan, baby
pronouns: he, they, yours, we, myself

2. a. Bobby was going to be late to meet Lori and **he** didn't want to make her wait.
    b. Leni was designing a new outfit and **she** was very excited.
    c. Lynn wants to make a new team so **she** can play football after school.

Page 30: Creative writing

1. Use of narrator: pointing to the lines said by the narrator.
Speakers on the left: pointing to Lincoln and Clyde's names.
Stage directions: pointing to the stage directions in brackets.

2. Accept any script with use of narrator, character's names on the left and what they say on the right, their actions in brackets.

Page 31: Expanded noun phrases

1. a. shiny, new
    b. new, sparkly
    c. green, smelly
    d. dark, gloomy
    e. long, green
    f. sparkly, pink

2. a. in the lab
    b. underneath the sofa cushions
    c. on the mantel piece
    d. on the skateboard
    e. in the pizza oven
    f. down the catwalk

Page 32: Parts of a sentence
1. **Nouns:** diamond ring, tiara, shoes, lollypop, sequins, cake
   Verbs: running, sit, singing, dreaming, dribbling, jump, sleeping, yawning

2. **Adjectives:** pink, long, pretty
   Adverbs: quietly, quickly, slowly

3. a. in   d. on
   b. over   e. during
   c. in   f. since

Page 33: Spelling pattern -tion
1. action, animation, donation, disruption, instruction, affection, selection, rotation

2. a. station   d. injection
   b. addition   e. eruption
   c. invitation

Page 34: Editing and correcting
1. **Example:** Vampires are a type of ferocious monster. They cannot go out in sunlight and sleep during daylight. They have two sharp fangs. Garlic and silver can weaken a vampire. In addition, they can disappear when they click their fingers. Interestingly, vampires do not produce a reflection in mirrors, glass or other objects. Not many people believe in these creatures but I do.

Page 35: Paragraphs and headings
1. Where do bees live?
   What is the job of the Queen?
   What is the job of the worker bees?
   What is the job of the drones?
   (or similar)

2. a. false   c. false
   b. true   d. true

Page 36: Reading comprehension
1. a. He was excited because he woke early, wanted to jump on the bed and he ate quickly. He could be nervous because he walked quickly and his fingers shivered while he waited.

   b. The guest will say a speech or give a talk as there is a podium and a speaker set up on the stage.

   c. Because he was going to meet a special guest who is arriving in a stretch limousine and wanted to be smart.

Page 37: Direct speech
1. a. correct   d. incorrect
   b. incorrect   e. incorrect
   c. correct

2. a. "Lily's diaper needs changing again!" yelled Lana.
   b. "I've got awesome, new lyrics for a song," declared Luna.
   c. "I literally don't know what to wear!" moaned Lori.

Page 38: Plurals and possessives
1. a. possessive   d. possessive
   b. plural   e. possessive
   c. plural

2. Accept any correct sentences where pencil has been used both as a possessive and a plural.

Page 39: Plural apostrophes
1. a. witches' hats   c. fairies' stools
   b. frogs' legs   d. newts' eyes

2. a. people's hair   c. geese's feathers
   b. sheep's fleece   d. children's earwax

Page 40: Fronted adverbials
1. a. Last weekend, Lana and Lola decorated their room.
   b. Upstairs, Leni is trying to do her homework.
   c. Three times, Lincoln crashed his skateboard.
   d. Mysteriously, Lucy's lunch disappeared.

2. a. Early in the morning, all was quiet in the house.
   b. Frantically, Clyde tried to mop up his nosebleed.
   c. In the blink of an eye, Leni snatched a dress from my wardrobe.

Page 41: Point of view
1. a. I am the oldest.
   b. My team won.
   c. We are the youngest. or...
      Lily and I are the youngest.

2. I have created a new substance which removes sticky gum from any surface. It took me 27 tries to perfect the substance. I am excited to tell everyone about my incredible discovery.

Page 42: Reading comprehension
1. a. eleven
   b. Lily
   c. the middle child

2. Accept any answer which makes sense and is supported.

3. a. Yes because it is chaotic and there are lots of people.
   b. Yes, it says that they get along together and help each other out.

Page 43: Spelling tricky words
1. a. grammar   f. eighth
   b. accident   g. naughty
   c. sentence   h. library
   d. reign   i. knowledge
   e. February

2. a. grammar   c. library
   b. accident   d. February

3. a. grammar   e. February
   b. eighth   f. naughty
   c. sentence   g. knowledge
   d. reign   h. library

Page 44: Cinquain poetry
1. Accept any suitable poem which matches the success criteria for a cinquain.

2. Accept the poem in best handwriting.

Page 45: Fronted adverbials
1. **Time:** Next year, After a while, On Saturday
   Manner: Without warning, Awkwardly, As fast as he could
   place: Back at the house, On the street, Far away

2. a. incorrect   c. correct
   b. correct   d. incorrect